Some of the Parts

⊕Britannica

ENCYCLOPÆDIA BRITANNICA EDUCATIONAL CORPORATION

Mathematics in Context is a comprehensive curriculum for the middle grades. It was developed in collaboration with the Wisconsin Center for Education Research, School of Education, University of Wisconsin–Madison and the Freudenthal Institute at the University of Utrecht, The Netherlands, with the support of National Science Foundation Grant No. 9054928.

National Science Foundation

Opinions expressed are those of the authors
and not necessarily those of the Foundation

ISBN 0-7826-1500-7
1 2 3 4 5 6 7 8 9 10   99 98 97

The *Mathematics in Context* Development Team

Mathematics in Context is a comprehensive curriculum for the middle grades. The National Science Foundation funded the National Center for Research in Mathematical Sciences Education at the University of Wisconsin–Madison to develop and field test the materials from 1991 through 1996. The Freudenthal Institute at the University of Utrecht in The Netherlands, as a subcontractor, collaborated with the University of Wisconsin–Madison on the development of the curriculum.

National Center for Research in Mathematical Sciences Education Staff

Thomas A. Romberg
Director

Joan Daniels Pedro
Assistant to the Director

Gail Burrill
Coordinator
Field Test Materials

Margaret Meyer
Coordinator
Pilot Test Materials

Mary Ann Fix
Editorial Coordinator

Sherian Foster
Editorial Coordinator

James A. Middleton
Pilot Test Coordinator

Project Staff

Jonathan Brendefur
Laura J. Brinker
James Browne
Jack Burrill
Rose Byrd
Peter Christiansen
Barbara Clarke
Doug Clarke
Beth R. Cole

Fae Dremock
Jasmina Milinkovic
Margaret A. Pligge
Mary C. Shafer
Julia A. Shew
Aaron N. Simon
Marvin Smith
Stephanie Z. Smith
Mary S. Spence

Freudenthal Institute Staff

Jan de Lange
Director

Els Feijs
Coordinator

Martin van Reeuwijk
Coordinator

Project Staff

Mieke Abels
Nina Boswinkel
Frans van Galen
Koeno Gravemeijer
Marja van den Heuvel-Panhuizen
Jan Auke de Jong
Vincent Jonker
Ronald Keijzer

Martin Kindt
Jansie Niehaus
Nanda Querelle
Anton Roodhardt
Leen Streefland
Adri Treffers
Monica Wijers
Astrid de Wild

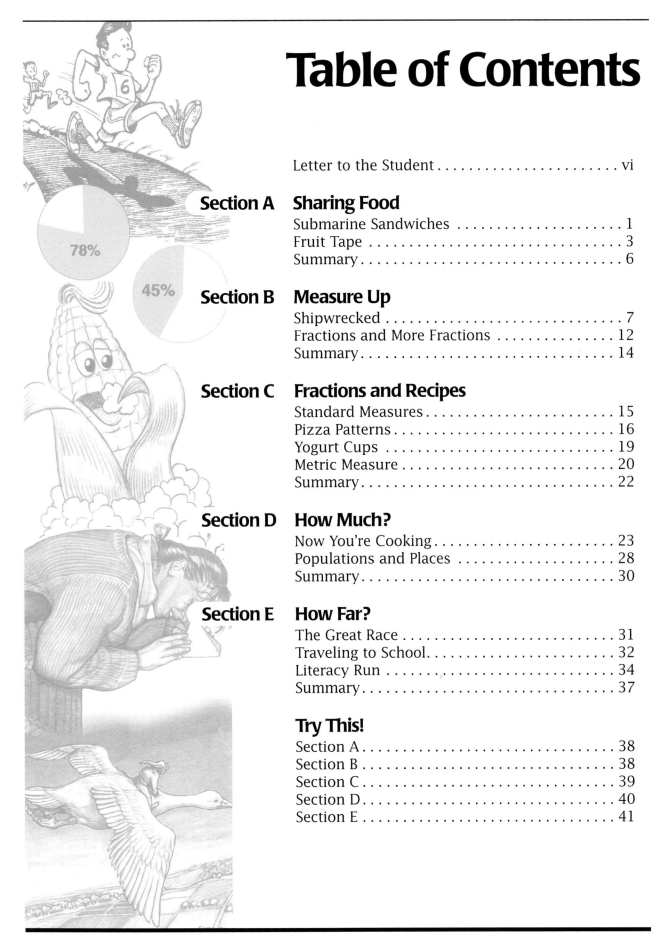

Table of Contents

Dear Student,

Welcome to *Some of the Parts.*

In this unit, you will learn how the parts of quantities and objects we call fractions relate to the whole.

You will use fractions to measure and combine quantities of milk. Will $\frac{1}{3}$ of a can of milk and $\frac{5}{8}$ of a can of milk fit into one can?

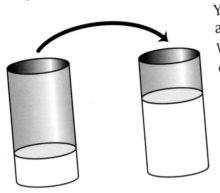

Knowing about relationships between fractions will help you alter recipes to serve different numbers of people.

You will also learn how fractions can help you measure and calculate distances.

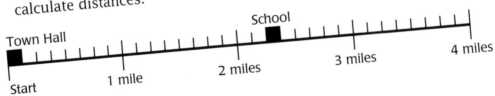

In the end, you should understand something about relationships between fractions. You will also use your understanding of fractions to add, subtract, multiply, and divide with them.

Sincerely,

The Mathematics in Context Development Team

SUBMARINE *Sandwiches*

At Booker T. Washington Middle School, a class is planning a nature hike. The class is divided into groups of students. Each group of students pools their money to buy submarine sandwiches for lunch. When lunchtime arrives, each group shares the subs *equally.*

Above, you see four groups and the number of subs they have to share.

1. In which group do the students get the most to eat? Explain your answer.

2. In which group do the students get the least to eat? Explain your answer.

Emmy gets . . . ?

3. Use the rectangles beside each picture on **Student Activity Sheet 1** to show how the sandwiches should be cut so that each student in the group gets an equal share. Color the piece or pieces for Emmy, Jake, Sandra, and Walter. Then use *fractions* to describe how much each person will get.

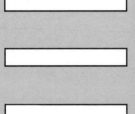

Jake gets . . . . . ?

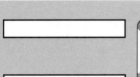

Sandra gets . . ?

4. Draw two other pictures of students with submarine sandwiches. Choose your own numbers for students and sandwiches. Show how the sandwiches could be shared equally. Describe with fractions how much each student will get.

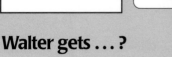

Walter gets . . . ?

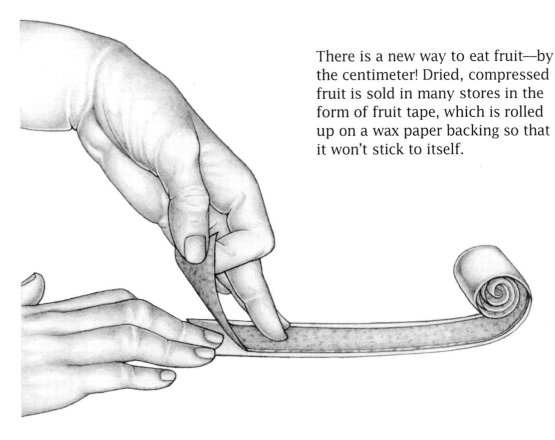

There is a new way to eat fruit—by the centimeter! Dried, compressed fruit is sold in many stores in the form of fruit tape, which is rolled up on a wax paper backing so that it won't stick to itself.

2 equal pieces	4 equal pieces	8 equal pieces	3 equal pieces	6 equal pieces	5 equal pieces

5. On **Student Activity Sheet 2,** you will find drawings of six pieces of fruit tape. Cut them out.

Divide and cut each fruit tape into the number of pieces indicated on **Student Activity Sheet 3.** Be sure that your pieces are equal. Glue the pieces onto the bars on **Student Activity Sheet 3.** Label each piece with a fraction. Be prepared to explain how you decided where to cut.

6. Ten children want to share one fruit tape. Which fruit tape on **Student Activity Sheet 3** can you use to show how much each of them will get?

7. Two children want to share one fruit tape. Which tape can you use to show how much each will get? Are there several possibilities?

8. Three children want to share one fruit tape. Which tapes can you use to show how much each will get?

Edward was in a group of four. He got his equal share of one fruit tape. You can see it in his hand in the drawing below.

9. Draw a picture of the whole fruit tape. Explain how you figured out how long to make your drawing.

Summary

When you divide something into equal parts, you can name the parts with fractions.

This whole sub can be divided into three equal parts.

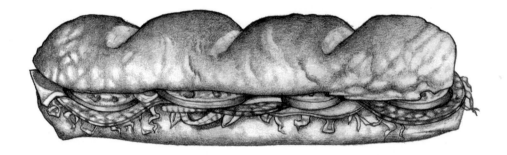

These parts can be called *thirds*. There are three parts. Each part is one-third of the whole.

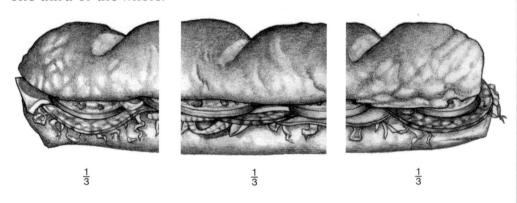

$\frac{1}{3}$ $\frac{1}{3}$ $\frac{1}{3}$

Summary Questions

10. a. List some of the fractions you worked with in this section.

     b. Describe how some of the fractions you listed might be related to each other.

Shipwrecked

You and a couple of friends are on a boat trip in the Pacific. Unfortunately, your boat hits a coral reef and begins to sink. You and your friends are able to swim to a nearby island.

When you explore the island, you discover that it offers a variety of food: coconut milk, all sorts of berries, and several kinds of fruit.

You are very lucky! Some tin cans have washed ashore. This makes the coconut milk easier to drink and allows you to share it when the coconut supply is low.

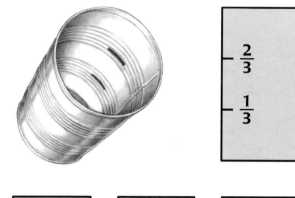

$$\frac{2}{3}$$

$$\frac{1}{3}$$

Sometimes you find that you want less than a whole can of coconut milk, so you scratch lines inside the cans as pictured on the left.

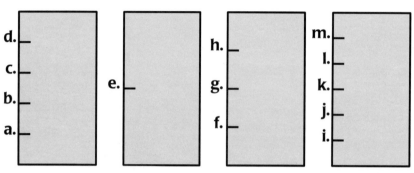

1. In your notebook, write the fractions that you would put beside the measuring points labeled *a* through *m*.

In a fraction, the number written above the line segment is called the **numerator**.

The number written below the line segment is called the **denominator**.

$$\frac{2}{3} \begin{array}{l} \Leftarrow \textit{numerator} \\ \Leftarrow \textit{denominator} \end{array}$$

2. Explain what the numerator and denominator in a fraction mean.

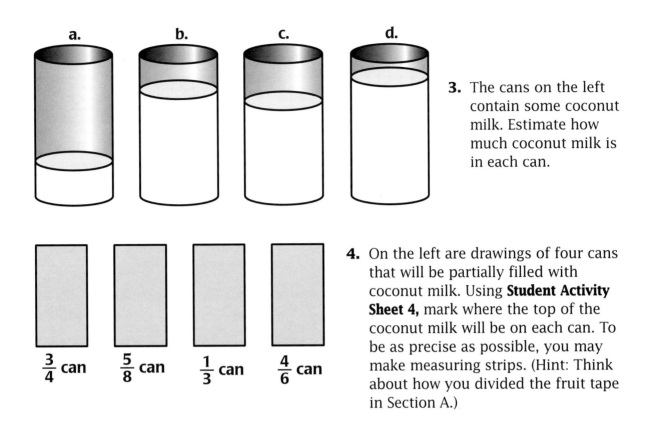

$\frac{3}{4}$ can $\frac{5}{8}$ can $\frac{1}{3}$ can $\frac{4}{6}$ can

3. The cans on the left contain some coconut milk. Estimate how much coconut milk is in each can.

4. On the left are drawings of four cans that will be partially filled with coconut milk. Using **Student Activity Sheet 4,** mark where the top of the coconut milk will be on each can. To be as precise as possible, you may make measuring strips. (Hint: Think about how you divided the fruit tape in Section A.)

5. Collect some tin cans that are all the same size. Mark measuring lines on each can to show halves, thirds, fourths, sixths, eighths, and twelfths.

6. Suppose you have two cans of the same size that are partially filled with coconut milk. One can is $\frac{1}{2}$ full, and the other one is $\frac{1}{3}$ full. You want to pour the milk from the two cans into one empty can of the same size. Will one can hold all of this milk? How do you know?

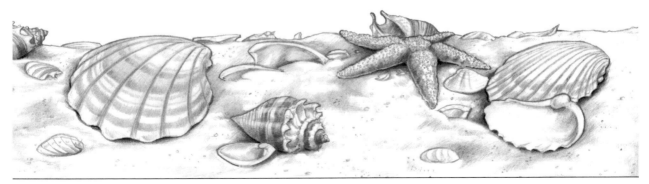

Pete and Marge are on the island with you. Marge's can is filled $\frac{3}{4}$ of the way with coconut milk. Pete's can is filled $\frac{1}{3}$ of the way with coconut milk. They want to figure out if it is possible to put the contents of both cans together into one can of the same size.

Pete solves the problem in the following manner:

IF A CAN IS $\frac{3}{4}$ FULL, THERE IS STILL ROOM FOR $\frac{1}{4}$ OF A CAN. SINCE $\frac{1}{3}$ OF A CAN IS MORE THAN $\frac{1}{4}$ OF A CAN, I THINK THE COCONUT MILK WILL OVERFLOW.

Marge thinks about the problem in this way:

IF YOU DRAW THE TWO CANS AND SHADE THE AMOUNT OF MILK IN EACH, YOU CAN SEE THAT THE MILK IN CAN 2 WILL NOT ALL FIT INTO CAN 1.

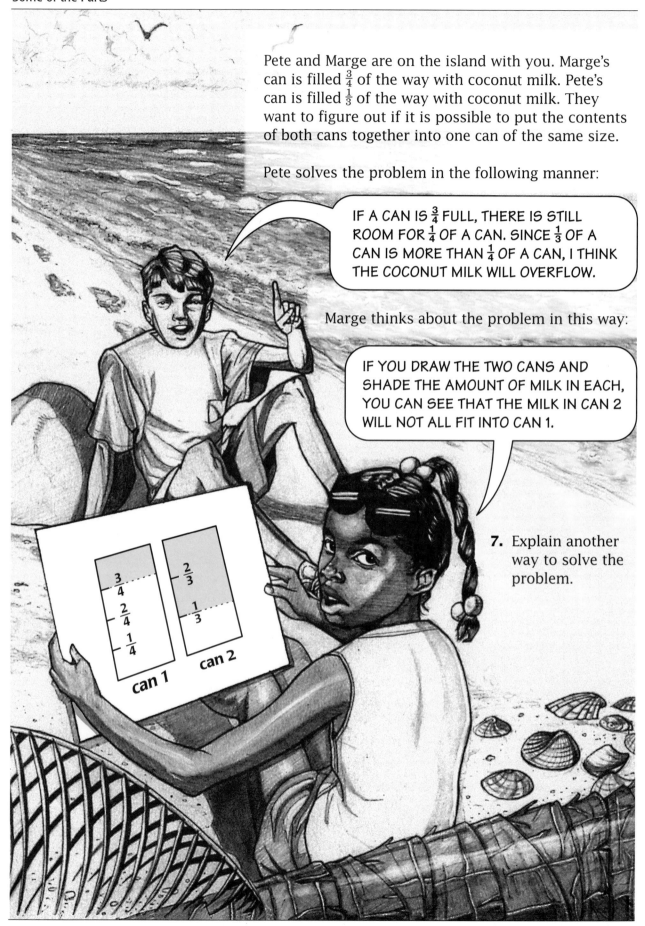

7. Explain another way to solve the problem.

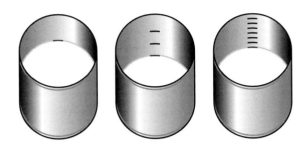
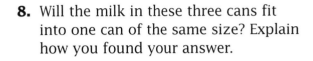

Suppose you have three cans of the same size partially filled with coconut milk. One can is $\frac{1}{2}$ full, the second is $\frac{1}{4}$ full, and the third is $\frac{1}{8}$ full.

8. Will the milk in these three cans fit into one can of the same size? Explain how you found your answer.

9. You have a can that is $\frac{1}{2}$ full, a can that is $\frac{1}{3}$ full, and a can that is $\frac{1}{4}$ full. Without pouring, how can you find out if the milk in these three cans will fit into one can of the same size?

can **a**	can **b**	can **c**
$\frac{2}{3}$	$\frac{1}{2}$	$\frac{1}{3}$
full	full	full

can **d**	can **e**	can **f**
$\frac{1}{4}$	$\frac{1}{6}$	$\frac{1}{8}$
full	full	full

10. Suppose you have the six equal-sized cans of coconut milk shown on the left. The milk will not all fit into one can, but you can combine the milk of some of the cans. Write at least five combinations of cans whose milk could be poured together into one can of the same size. The milk does not have to fill a can completely.

11. Suppose you have two cans of the same size. One is $\frac{3}{4}$ full, and the other is $\frac{1}{4}$ full. If you combine the contents of the two cans, you will exactly fill one can of the same size. Find five ways to exactly fill one can using the cans in problem **10**. You may use cans more than once for each solution. Check your answers by using real cans.

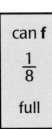

FRACTION TIMES

Shipwrecked Kids Rescued

FRACTIONS *and* MORE FRACTIONS

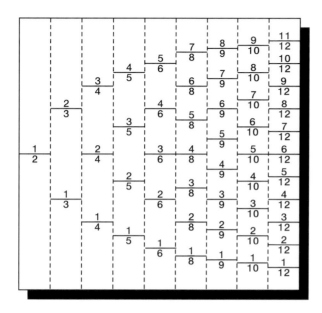

Suppose you have nine tin cans of the same size. Each can has the same height as the measuring strips on **Student Activity Sheet 5.** You can use these strips to draw measuring lines inside the cans.

Cut out the strips on **Student Activity Sheet 5.** Use the strips to find out what will happen if you pour coconut milk from two or more cans into one can.

12. a. Suppose you poured $\frac{1}{3}$ of a can of milk and $\frac{1}{2}$ of a can of milk into another can of the same size. How can you use your fraction strips to find how full the other can will be?

b. Explain why this sentence is correct: $\frac{1}{3}$ can $+ \frac{1}{2}$ can $= \frac{5}{6}$ can.

13. a. Use the strips to find at least six fraction combinations like the one in problem **12b.** Write a sentence for each.

b. For each sentence, explain why it is correct.

You may have included a sentence in problem **13** with an outcome of more than one, such as this sentence: $\frac{3}{4}$ can $+ \frac{1}{2}$ can $= 1\frac{1}{4}$ can.

Numbers like $1\frac{1}{4}$ are called ***mixed numbers***.

14. Why do you think numbers like $1\frac{1}{4}$ and $2\frac{3}{5}$ are called *mixed numbers*?

Devin, a student in Ms. Wood's class, wrote the following sentence:

$$\tfrac{3}{4} \text{ can} + \tfrac{1}{2} \text{ can} = \tfrac{5}{4} \text{ can}$$

15. Is Devin's sentence correct? Explain.

Devin and Becky both lost their paper strips from **Student Activity Sheet 5.** They made the new strips you see below.

16. a. Are both sets of strips okay to use to measure amounts of coconut milk? Explain why or why not.

b. Devin found a quarter strip from **Student Activity Sheet 5.** How can Devin decide whether or not he can use this strip with the new strips he just made to solve fraction problems?

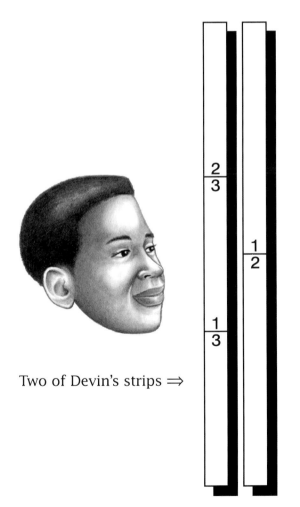

Two of Devin's strips ⇒

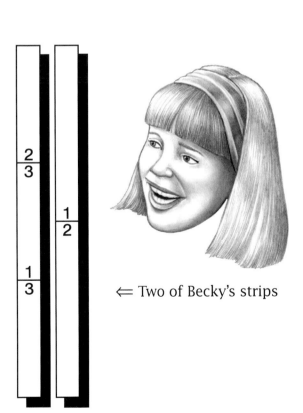

⇐ Two of Becky's strips

Summary

When a whole is divided equally into parts, you can use fractions to describe the parts. The top number in a fraction is called the *numerator.* The bottom number is called the *denominator.*

It is possible to combine fractions. One possibility is:

$$\tfrac{1}{2} \text{ can} + \tfrac{1}{4} \text{ can} = \tfrac{3}{4} \text{ can}$$

Measuring strips can help you combine fractions. If you write fractions beside measuring points on cans, you usually do it like this:

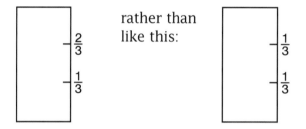

rather than like this:

Summary Questions

You and your friends are sharing subs. You get $\frac{4}{3}$ of a sub. One of your friends gets $\frac{2}{3}$ of a sub.

17. a. What does $\frac{4}{3}$ mean?

   b. How is $\frac{2}{3}$ related to $\frac{4}{3}$?

18. Look at the numerators in the sentence $\frac{1}{2}$ can $+\frac{1}{4}$ can $=\frac{3}{4}$ can. How is it possible to get a 3 as the numerator?

19. You and a friend go out for pizza. You order a 10-inch pepperoni pizza and an 8-inch cheese pizza. Both pizzas are cut into eight equal slices. You eat six pepperoni and two cheese slices. Your friend eats the rest. Who ate more pizza, you or your friend? Explain.

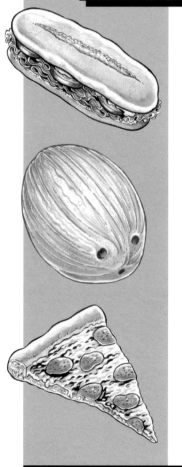

Standard Measures

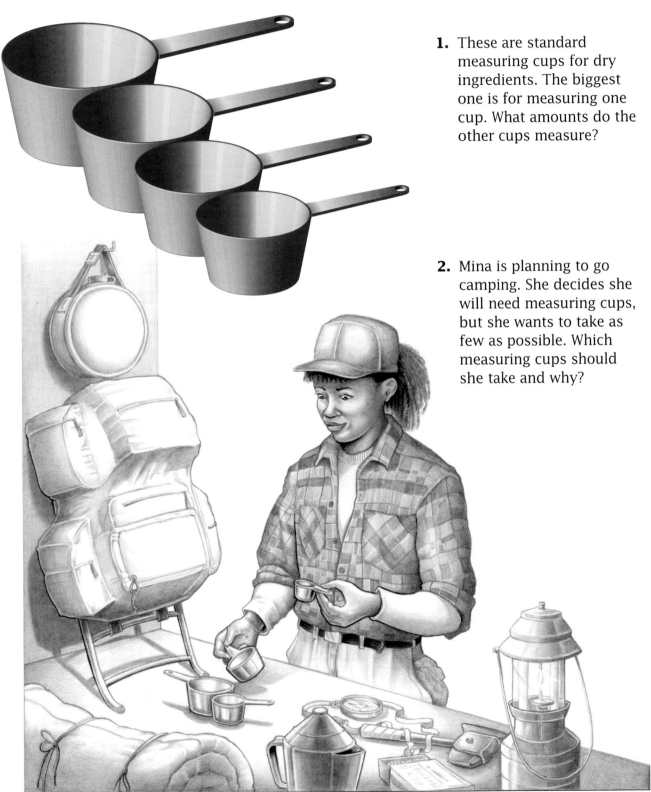

1. These are standard measuring cups for dry ingredients. The biggest one is for measuring one cup. What amounts do the other cups measure?

2. Mina is planning to go camping. She decides she will need measuring cups, but she wants to take as few as possible. Which measuring cups should she take and why?

Juan found the following pizza recipe.

Pizza Patterns

Makes 4 pizzas.

Ingredients
1 8-fl oz jar of spaghetti sauce
1 lb ground beef
$\frac{1}{3}$ cup dry bread crumbs
$\frac{1}{2}$ tsp dried oregano
2 pitted ripe olives
$\frac{1}{4}$ cup shredded mozzarella cheese
$\frac{1}{4}$ cup shredded cheddar cheese
4 mushrooms

Utensils
Liquid measuring cup
Medium bowl
Dry measuring cup
Measuring spoons
Fork
Shallow baking pan, $15\frac{1}{2}'' \times 10\frac{1}{2}''$
Ruler
Spatula
Sharp knife
Cutting board
Pot holders

1. Preheat oven to 425°F.
2. Measure $\frac{1}{2}$ cup (4 fl oz) from the jar of spaghetti sauce. Save the rest of the jar of sauce.
3. Add the $\frac{1}{2}$ cup spaghetti sauce, 1 lb ground beef, $\frac{1}{3}$ cup dry bread crumbs, and $\frac{1}{2}$ teaspoon dried oregano to bowl and stir with a fork until mixed together. Divide the mixture into four equal balls. Place each ball several inches apart in the baking pan.
4. Pat each ball into a $4\frac{1}{2}$-inch circle. Pinch the edge of each circle to make a rim.
5. Pour about 2 tablespoons of the remaining spaghetti sauce into the center of each circle and spread it to the edges with a spatula. Bake 15 to 20 minutes.
6. While the pizzas are baking, cut 2 pitted ripe olives and 4 mushrooms crosswise into 4 slices each.
7. Remove the pan from the oven.
8. Sprinkle each pizza with $\frac{1}{4}$ cup shredded mozzarella cheese and $\frac{1}{4}$ cup shredded cheddar cheese, dividing the cheese over the four pizzas. Make a pattern on each pizza using 4 mushroom slices and 2 olive slices per pizza.
9. Remove pizzas from the oven, turn the oven off, and let pizzas cool before eating.

HINT: BE CREATIVE AND USE YOUR FAVORITE FOODS TO MAKE ALL TYPES OF PATTERNS.

Juan makes a pizza and likes the taste of it so much that he decides to have a pizza party. He invites 23 friends. The recipe makes four pizzas, but Juan decides that he will need to make 24 pizza patterns. All of his friends love pizza.

3. What will Juan have to do to the amount of each ingredient to make 24 pizzas?

4. How much shredded cheddar cheese will he need to make 24 pizzas?

Number of Pizzas	4		
Teaspoons of Oregano	$\frac{1}{2}$		

Ming, one of Juan's friends, helps him prepare the food. She starts with the oregano. She makes a table to show how the amount of oregano will change as the number of pizzas changes.

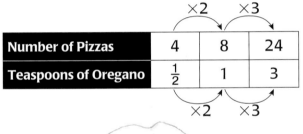

Number of Pizzas	4	8	24
Teaspoons of Oregano	$\frac{1}{2}$	1	3

Ming multiplies the number of pizzas and teaspoons of oregano by two and then multiplies again by three. The table on the left shows how Ming found the number of teaspoons of oregano needed for 24 pizzas.

Juan's friend Katrina looked at Ming's table and said,

YOU COULD HAVE DONE IT THIS WAY TOO.

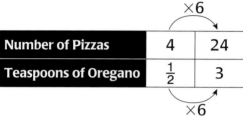

	×6	
Number of Pizzas	4	24
Teaspoons of Oregano	$\frac{1}{2}$	3

5. How did Katrina figure out that $\frac{1}{2} \times 6 = 3$?

Katrina figured out the amount of oregano needed for 24 pizzas in still another way.

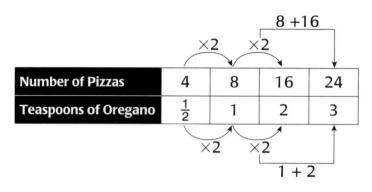

		8 +16	
	×2	×2	
Number of Pizzas	4	8	16	24
Teaspoons of Oregano	$\frac{1}{2}$	1	2	3
	×2	×2	
		1 + 2	

6. a. Explain Katrina's strategy.

b. How are Katrina's and Ming's strategies different? How are they alike?

Number of Pizzas	4		
Cups of Bread Crumbs	$\frac{1}{3}$		
Jars of Spaghetti Sauce	1		
Pounds of Ground Beef	1		
Teaspoons of Dried Oregano	$\frac{1}{2}$		
Number of Olives	2		
Cups of Shredded Mozzarella Cheese	$\frac{1}{4}$		
Cups of Shredded Cheddar Cheese	$\frac{1}{4}$		
Number of Mushrooms	4		

The tables Katrina and Ming made are called **ratio tables**. The table on the left is like a ratio table, except with more ingredients listed.

7. Complete the table on **Student Activity Sheet 6** so that Juan and his friends can make 24 pizza patterns.

Yogurt Cups

Makes 4 cups.

Ingredients

$\frac{3}{4}$ cup all-purpose flour
$\frac{1}{4}$ cup margarine or butter, softened
3 Tbs powdered sugar
2 to 3 Tbs cold water
$1\frac{1}{3}$ cups yogurt (any flavor)

1. Heat oven to 375°F.
2. Mix flour, margarine, and powdered sugar until crumbly. Sprinkle in water, 1 tsp at a time, stirring until dough forms.
3. Press about 3 Tbs of dough into each of 4 ungreased, 6-ounce custard cups, up to within $\frac{1}{2}$ inch of top.
4. Bake until golden brown, 10 to 12 minutes; let cool 10 minutes. Carefully remove pastries from cups with a small metal spatula; let cool completely on wire rack.
5. Fill each pastry cup with $\frac{1}{3}$ cup of yogurt; garnish with fresh fruit if desired.

Source: Recipe provided courtesy of Gold Medal® Flour.

Some of Juan's friends want to have dessert. Since the recipe on the left will only make enough yogurt cups for four people, Juan makes a chart to find the amounts of each ingredient he will need to serve more or fewer than four people.

Servings	4	2	8	6	10	16
Flour (cups)	$\frac{3}{4}$					
Margarine (cups)	$\frac{1}{4}$					
Powdered Sugar (tablespoons)	3					
Water (teaspoons)	$2\frac{1}{2}$					
Yogurt (cups)	$1\frac{1}{3}$					

8. Complete the table on **Student Activity Sheet 7** for the Yogurt Cups recipe.

9. There are different ways to find the amounts of ingredients for 10 servings. Describe two possibilities.

10. Is it possible to use containers other than cups and spoons to measure the ingredients for the yogurt cups recipe? Why or why not?

METRIC MEASURE

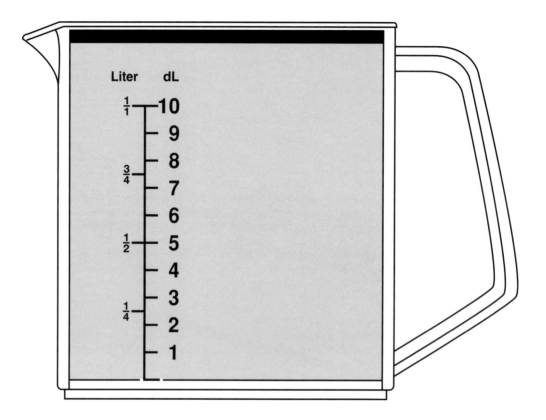

Above you see a picture of a measuring cup that is marked in liters and deciliters (dL).

11. How many deciliters are in one liter?

12. How many deciliters are in $\frac{1}{4}$ liter?

13. The measurements $\frac{1}{4}$ liter and $\frac{3}{4}$ liter are shown on the cup above. Why doesn't the drawing show $\frac{2}{4}$ liter?

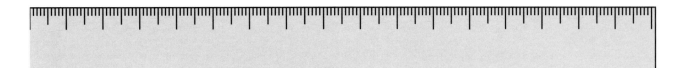

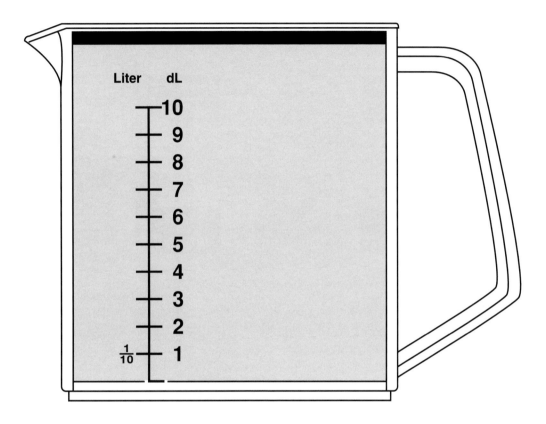

Here is another measuring cup.

14. a. What is the difference between the cup on page 20 and this cup?

   b. On **Student Activity Sheet 8**, write the fractions of a liter that correspond to the measuring lines pictured above.

15. Draw measuring lines for $\frac{1}{3}$ liter and $\frac{2}{3}$ liter on the measuring cup on **Student Activity Sheet 8.**

16. How many deciliters are in $\frac{1}{3}$ liter?

Summary

There are several ways to use the numbers in the columns of ratio tables to find the numbers in a new column.

Table 1
Multiplying

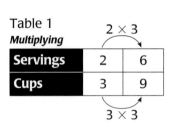

Servings	2	6
Cups	3	9

Table 3

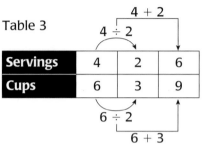

Servings	4	2	6
Cups	6	3	9

Table 2
Dividing

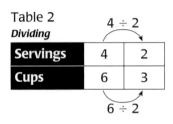

Servings	4	2
Cups	6	3

Table 4

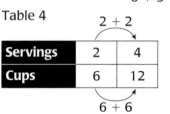

Servings	2	4
Cups	6	12

Often, it is useful to use a combination of methods.

Table 5

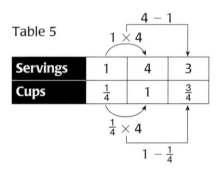

Servings	1	4	3
Cups	$\frac{1}{4}$	1	$\frac{3}{4}$

Summary Questions

17. **a.** Table 1 uses multiplying, and Table 2 uses dividing. What operations do Tables 3 and 4 use?

 b. Find another way to produce the third column in Table 5.

18. Find a recipe for your favorite dish. Make a table to show the amounts of ingredients needed to make different numbers of servings.

Now You're Cooking

Here is a recipe for a dish that Eileen and her mother are planning to make for dinner.

Chicken & Tortilla Casserole

Makes 8 servings.

Ingredients

8 skinless, boneless chicken breast halves
1 lb jar of salsa (any will do, but green salsa is very spicy)
1 cup light sour cream
$\frac{1}{2}$ cup half-and-half
12 tortillas (blue corn, corn, or flour)
4 cups (1 lb) shredded cheddar cheese
$\frac{1}{3}$ cup grated Parmesan cheese

Preheat oven to 350°F.

Rinse chicken with cold water. Fill half of a five-quart saucepan with water. Bring to a boil. Turn off burner, carefully add chicken, and cover. After 20 minutes, check the chicken: place one piece on the cutting board, cut to center of thickest part. If chicken is still pink inside, return it to pan, cover, and let stand for 10 more minutes. Repeat. When chicken is no longer pink in the center, place all chicken on cutting board. Cut into bite-size pieces. Place half of the chicken in a 9″ × 13″ baking pan. Cover with half of the salsa.

Mix sour cream with half-and-half until well blended. Spoon half of the mixture over chicken and salsa.

Cut tortillas into one-inch wide strips. Top sour cream mixture with half of the tortilla strips and half of the cheddar cheese.

Repeat all layers using remaining ingredients. Cover pan with foil. Fold foil around edges of pan to seal. Bake 40 minutes.

Remove from oven. Carefully remove foil, starting on side away from you. (Steam can burn.) Sprinkle top of casserole with Parmesan cheese. Return pan to oven. Bake, uncovered, for about 5 more minutes, until cheese is golden brown. Remove pan from oven. Let casserole stand for 10 minutes before serving.

Number of Servings	8	
Number of Chicken Breast Halves	8	
Jars of Salsa	1	
Cups of Light Sour Cream	1	
Cups of Half-and-Half	$\frac{1}{2}$	
Number of Corn Tortillas	12	
Cups of Shredded Cheddar Cheese	4	
Cups of Grated Parmesan Cheese	$\frac{1}{3}$	

Eileen and her mother are making dinner for themselves and two friends. The recipe for Chicken & Tortilla Casserole makes eight servings, but Eileen and her mother want to make the recipe for only four.

1. Use **Student Activity Sheet 9** to decide how much of each ingredient they will need.

A few months later it is Eileen's mother's birthday. Eileen decides to fix Chicken & Tortilla Casserole for her mother's birthday dinner.

2. Now Eileen is cooking dinner for only two people. How much will she need of each ingredient? You may extend your table from problem **1** if you wish.

The school cafeteria staff buys large quantities of food for lunches. After receiving a food shipment, the cafeteria staff divides it into the amounts needed for recipes (just like Eileen divided the casserole ingredients).

3. Use **Student Activity Sheet 10** to draw lines and color the piece on each food item that is needed by the cafeteria staff.

a. This piece of bologna weighs 400 grams. Cut off 100 grams.

b. This piece of salami weighs 600 grams. Cut off 450 grams.

c. This piece of cheese weighs 1,200 grams. Cut off 800 grams.

d. This piece of cheese weighs 1,600 grams. Cut off 1,200 grams.

e. This piece of sausage weighs 1,200 grams. Cut off 200 grams.

f. This piece of sausage weighs 900 grams. Cut off 100 grams.

g. This piece of pepperoni weighs 2,400 grams. Cut off 2,000 grams.

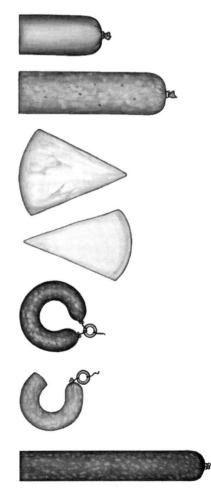

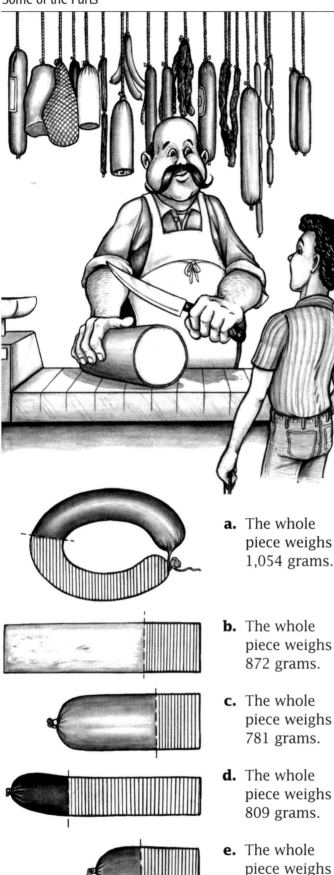

In the last set of problems, the weights of the pieces of meat and cheese were rounded to the nearest 100 or 50 grams. If you weigh a piece of meat on an electronic balance, the weight could be rounded to the nearest gram.

Abe is shopping at a market where they sell food that is not yet packaged. Abe goes to a stand and asks, "May I have 200 grams of bologna?" The butcher takes the piece of bologna from the case and weighs it. The scale indicates that the piece weighs 623 grams. The butcher thinks, "I need about one-third of it."

Before cutting, the butcher shows Abe the piece that is going to be cut off and asks, "Do you want a piece about this size?" Abe agrees that the piece is about the right size, so it is cut, and Abe buys the bologna.

a. The whole piece weighs 1,054 grams.

b. The whole piece weighs 872 grams.

c. The whole piece weighs 781 grams.

d. The whole piece weighs 809 grams.

e. The whole piece weighs 618 grams.

4. On the left you see some pieces of sausage and cheese. The dotted lines indicate where the butcher will cut. Estimate how much the cutoff piece (the part with the vertical lines) will weigh.

A full box of the cornflakes pictured on the right weighs 12 ounces.

5. What if some of the cornflakes have been eaten? Do you have to weigh the box to know the weight of what is left? Find another way to make an estimate.

Activity

Collect some boxes of food, such as flour, cereal, rice, and so on. The boxes may be full or empty. Mark the beginning level (real or made-up) of the food on the outside of the box. Use another color to draw in some lines that may help you estimate the weights of different levels of food. You may want to draw in quarters, thirds, or other divisions. Label each line with the fraction it represents. Now label each line again, this time with the weight represented by that line.

6. a. How much would food at each of the levels you marked weigh? How do you know?

   b. Why did you choose the fractions you did?

   c. Do you think now that you chose the best fractions for your lines? Why or why not?

Populations and *Places*

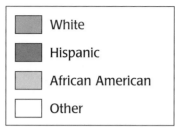

White

Hispanic

African American

Other

Most towns have people of different cultures. Below you see a diagram of one town's population. This kind of diagram is based on a fraction bar and can be called a *population bar*.

7. Use fractions to describe the cultural makeup of this town.

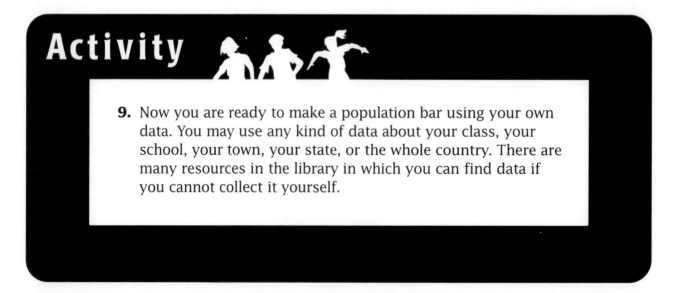

A group of students decided to make a population bar to show the population of their school. You can see the numbers they found on the left.

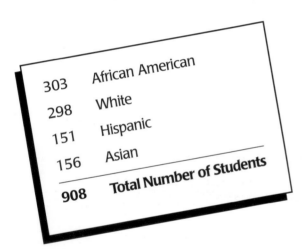

303	African American
298	White
151	Hispanic
156	Asian
908	**Total Number of Students**

8. a. Make a population bar for the school. Remember to add a key, explaining what each part stands for. You do not have to be precise.

b. Use your population bar to write fractions that describe the cultural makeup of the school.

Activity

9. Now you are ready to make a population bar using your own data. You may use any kind of data about your class, your school, your town, your state, or the whole country. There are many resources in the library in which you can find data if you cannot collect it yourself.

Sullivanville was founded by Irish settlers. Today this is still obvious in the many Irish names in the town. Some students counted the Irish names in the class lists of two different middle schools in the town. These are the results:

Robert Fulton School: 206 Irish names (school population: 806 students)

Jane Hull School: 98 Irish names (school population: 305 students)

10. Which school has more students with Irish names? Explain your answer.

The Main Street Plaza

The Commodore Building

People have different reactions to the new Main Street Plaza. One well-known architect said she thinks it is ugly and too different from the style of the rest of the buildings on Main Street.

However, the newspaper's opinion poll reveals that $\frac{2}{3}$ of the citizens like the look of the Main Street Plaza. Asked for their opinion about the Commodore building on Main Street, five out of eight people say that they like it.

11. In the newspaper clipping above, you read what people think about two new buildings in a town, the Main Street Plaza and the Commodore building. Which of the two buildings do more people like? Explain your answer.

Summary

In this section you:

- reduced the number of servings of food by halving a recipe,
- showed how much meat or cheese would be cut off of a whole piece, knowing the total weight and the weight of the amount to be cut off,
- used population bars to describe the cultural makeup of towns.

Summary Questions

12. How are the problems in this section related to the concept of fractions?

13. a. If the large bar of chocolate below weighs 95 kilograms, about how much does the shaded part weigh?

b. Explain how you found the weight of the shaded part of chocolate.

The Great Race

Cedarberg and Poplarville have an annual race on the highway that connects the two towns. The total length of the race is 36 kilometers. The Cedarberg Middle School track team will organize the water stations along the length of the race. One team member will work at each station.

Station	Team Member	Distance from Start
A	Cassie	$\frac{1}{3}$
B	Jami	$\frac{2}{3}$
C	J.R.	$\frac{1}{2}$
D	Scott	$\frac{3}{4}$
E	Lou	$\frac{1}{4}$

1. As the runners compete, which station will they come to first? Which will be second, third, and so on?

The students not assigned to work at the water stations are making a map to advertise the race, show the route, and indicate the locations of the water stations. To begin, they copy a map of the highway between the two towns. Then they decorate the map with some drawings.

2. Complete the map on **Student Activity Sheet 11** for the students by showing where the water stations will be.

Traveling to SCHOOL

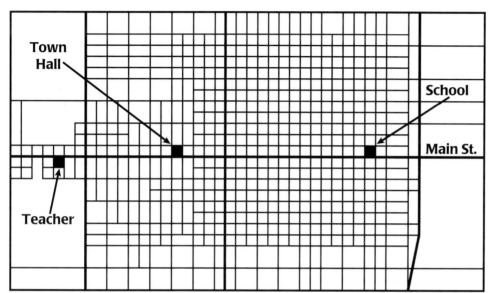

The city blocks in Cedarberg are $\frac{1}{8}$ of a mile long. Every morning, Belinda bikes the $1\frac{1}{2}$ miles from her home to school.

Sylvia lives only $\frac{1}{4}$ of a mile from school, so she walks there.

3. How many city blocks does Sylvia have to walk to get to school? How do you know?

4. How many city blocks does Belinda have to bike to get from her home to school? How did you figure it out?

5. Locate on the city map on **Student Activity Sheet 12** where Belinda and Sylvia could live.

Mihn lives 13 blocks from school, at the corner of Lincoln Avenue and Main Street.

6. How many miles does Mihn live from school? Explain how you know.

Michael lives in the same block as the Town Hall, which is 17 blocks west of the school.

7. How many miles does Michael have to travel to get to school? How did you figure it out?

As you can see on the city map, a teacher lives on the far west side of Cedarberg. Her home is $3\frac{1}{2}$ miles from school.

8. How many city blocks does she live from school?

9. a. How many city blocks are there in 5 miles?

b. How many city blocks are there in $2\frac{1}{4}$ miles?

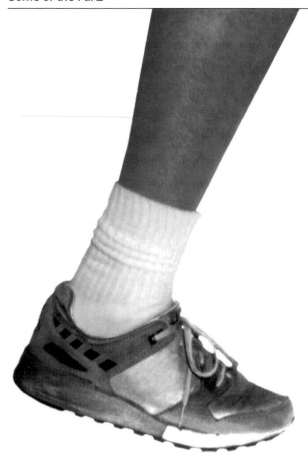

Literacy *RUN*

The track team had so much fun working together for the Cedarberg–Poplarville run, they decided to organize another run to raise money for the local literacy group. They decide to run a stretch of $1\frac{1}{8}$ miles along Main Street.

Below you see an enlargement of the map of Main Street. The run will begin at the Town Hall.

10. Mark the turnaround point for the run on **Student Activity Sheet 12.**

Town Hall							School						

Town Hall   School

Start   1 mile   2 miles   3 miles   4 miles

All of the kids in Cedarberg are invited to participate in the Literacy Run. They may run as many stretches as they wish. A stretch is either from the Town Hall to the turnaround point or from the turnaround point back to the Town Hall. Jami, for instance, wants to run five stretches:

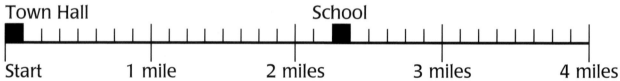

Town Hall — turnaround — Town Hall — turnaround — Town Hall — turnaround

or $5 \times 1\frac{1}{8}$ miles.

11. Here is a list of some of the kids from Cedarberg, with the number of stretches they intend to run. Copy this table into your notebook. Find how many miles each of them is going to run.

Balaji 2	stretches	$2 \times 1\frac{1}{8}$	= ___?___	miles
Meg 4	stretches	___?___	= ___?___	miles
Jami 5	stretches	___?___	= ___?___	miles
Julia 3	stretches	___?___	= ___?___	miles
Mary 8	stretches	___?___	= ___?___	miles
Rodolfo . . 6	stretches	___?___	= ___?___	miles

Some people prefer to write $2\frac{2}{8}$ miles as $2\frac{1}{4}$ miles.

12. a. Why are $2\frac{2}{8}$ miles and $2\frac{1}{4}$ miles the same distance?

b. Look at your answers to problem **11.** Is it possible to write any of them in a different way without changing their meaning? If so, provide two examples.

13. a. Copy the ratio table below into your notebook and fill it in.

b. Rodolfo plans to run 10 stretches. How can he use the ratio table below to find out how many miles he will be running?

Stretches	1	2	3	4			
Miles	$1\frac{1}{8}$						

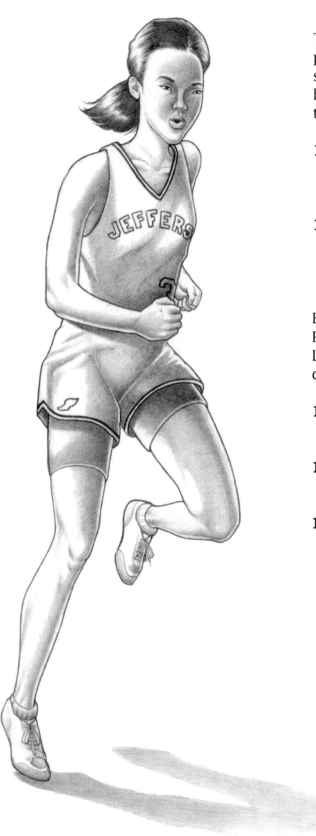

To raise money for the literacy group, the participants have to find people who will sponsor them. Meg, Mary, and Rodolfo each have pledges totaling $5.25 for each stretch they run.

14. How much money will each of them collect if they run all of their stretches?

15. Jami collected $21. How much did she get for each stretch?

Brenda is training for next year's Cedarberg–Poplarville race. She wants to use the Literacy Run as extra training, so she decides to run about 18 miles.

16. How many stretches does Brenda have to run?

17. Del wants to run about 8 miles. How many stretches should he plan to run?

18. How many stretches would it take to cover $13\frac{1}{8}$ miles?

Summary

Many different things can be divided into equal parts and named with fractions. When distances are measured, fractions can be used because a measurement unit can be divided into equal parts.

Ratio tables and *fraction strips* are tools that can be helpful when you work with fractions.

Summary Questions

19. Ms. Cole's class decides to order a giant submarine sandwich for the end-of-the-year picnic. They wonder if one sandwich 78 inches long will serve all 25 people in the class. If a serving is $3\frac{3}{4}$ inches, will there be enough? How could you defend your answer to the class?

20. Another class decides that each person in the class should receive $3\frac{1}{3}$ inches of a giant submarine sandwich. If there are 24 people in the class, how long does the giant submarine sandwich need to be to serve them all?

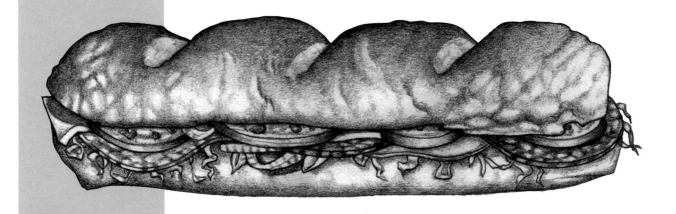

Section A. Sharing Food

1. Draw pictures that represent one-half and three-fourths. Write in words what your pictures show.

2. Draw four rectangles like those below and use them to show how the sandwiches in the picture should be cut so that each student in the group gets an equal share. How much of a sandwich will each person get?

3. Margarita is in a group of seven people. Shown below is her equal share of one fruit tape. Draw a picture of the whole fruit tape.

Section B. Measure Up

1. Explain what the numerator and denominator in $\frac{5}{8}$ mean.

2. Shanita claims that $\frac{3}{4}$ can $+ \frac{3}{8}$ can $= 1\frac{1}{8}$ cans. Is she correct? Use your fraction strips to explain.

3. Use your fraction strips to find the following sums:

   a. $\frac{1}{2}$ can $+ \frac{2}{5}$ can

   b. $\frac{2}{3}$ can $+ \frac{1}{4}$ can

4. Tanya had $\frac{5}{6}$ can. Name two measurements that she might have combined.

Section C. Fractions and Recipes

1. Jovita knows that in order to make four pizzas, she will need $\frac{1}{4}$ teaspoon of oregano. Jovita needs to figure out the amount of oregano needed to make 16 pizzas.

   a. What will Jovita have to do to the amount of oregano to make 16 pizzas?

   b. How much oregano will she need to make 24 pizzas?

Servings	4	16	24
Teaspoons	$\frac{1}{4}$	?	?

2. Jerome is making pancakes for his seven friends. Copy and complete the table below so that Jerome and his seven friends can have 18 pancakes. How many pancakes will each person get if each receives the same amount?

Pancakes	6	?	?
Mix (cups)	1	?	?
Water (cups)	$\frac{3}{4}$	?	?
Eggs	2	?	?
Oil (cups)	$\frac{1}{4}$	?	?

3. Use the ratio table below to solve the following problems.

Servings	3	9	27
Cups	5	15	45

   a. Find a way to produce the second column.

   b. Find a way to produce the third column.

Section D. How Much?

1. The piece of cheese below weighs 800 grams. Trace the piece and shade it to show 600 grams.

2. The piece of salami below weighs 726 grams. Estimate how much the part with the vertical lines weighs.

Section E. How Far?

1. Look at the map of Cooneyville below. The city blocks are $\frac{1}{9}$ of a mile long.

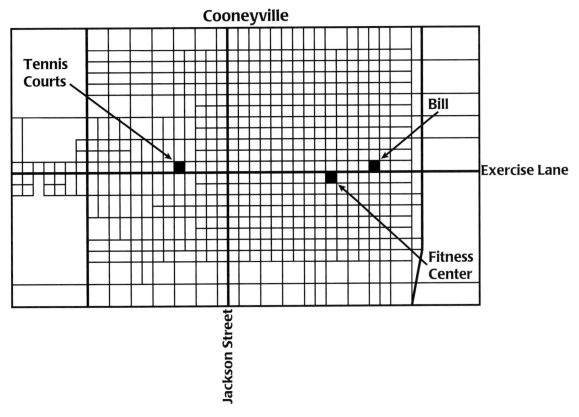

Cooneyville

a. How many miles does Bill live from the tennis courts?

b. What place is exactly 1 mile from the corner of Jackson Street and Exercise Lane?

c. How many city blocks are there in 4 miles?

d. How many city blocks are there in $5\frac{1}{3}$ miles? (Hint: You might want to use your fraction strips.)

2. A group of six friends decided to make and share a submarine sandwich. They decided that each person should receive $4\frac{1}{4}$ inches of a giant sub. How long does the sandwich have to be to serve them all?

CREDITS

Cover

Design by Ralph Paquet/Encyclopædia Britannica Educational Corporation.

Collage by Koorosh Jamalpur/KJ Graphics.

Title Page

Illustration by Paul Tucker/Encyclopædia Britannica Educational Corporation.

Illustrations

1–3 Paul Tucker/Encyclopædia Britannica Educational Corporation; **4 (bottom)** Phil Geib/ Encyclopædia Britannica Educational Corporation; **4 (top), 5** Brent Cardillo/Encyclopædia Britannica Educational Corporation; **6** Paul Tucker/Encyclopædia Britannica Educational Corporation; **7** Jerome Gordon/Encyclopædia Britannica Educational Corporation; **8–9** Phil Geib/Encyclopædia Britannica Educational Corporation; **10, 12** Jerome Gordon/ Encyclopædia Britannica Educational Corporation; **13** Phil Geib/Encyclopædia Britannica Educational Corporation; **14** Paul Tucker/Encyclopædia Britannica Educational Corporation; **15 (bottom), 16–19, 23–27, 31–33** Phil Geib/Encyclopædia Britannica Educational Corporation; **35** Jerome Gordon; **36** Brent Cardillo/Encyclopædia Britannica Educational Corporation; **37** Paul Tucker/Encyclopædia Britannica Educational Corporation.

Photographs

34 © David Alexovich/Encyclopædia Britannica Educational Corporation.